Distributors:
Music Sales Limited
8-9 Frith Street
London W1V 5TZ
England
Music Sales Pty Limited
120 Rothschild Avenue
Rosebery, NSW 2018
Australia

Order No. AM944647
ISBN 0-7119-6662-1

Wise Publications
London/New York/Paris
Sydney/Copenhagen/Madrid

COMPILED BY PETER EVANS
DESIGN BY PEARCE MARCHBANK
AND BEN MAY, STUDIO TWENTY

COVER AND TEXT IMAGES BASED ON
PHOTOGRAPHS BY SANDRA JOHNSON/RETNA

PRINTED IN GREAT BRITAIN BY
PRINTWISE (HAVERHILL) LIMITED, HAVERHILL, SU

Visit the Internet Music Shop
http://www.musicsales.co.uk

The
CELINE DION
Collection

ALL BY MYSELF

Words by Eric Carmen. Music by Sergei Rachmaninov & Eric Carmen.

8

BECAUSE YOU LOVED ME

Words & Music by Diane Warren.

love I found__ in you,__ I'll be for- ev - er thank - ful, ba - - - by.
love, I had__ it all.__ I'm grate - ful for__ each day__ you gave__ me.

You're the one__ who held__ me up, nev - er let__ me fall.__
May - be I__ don't know__ that much, but I know this much__ is true.__

You're the one__ who saw__ me through, through it all.__
I was blessed__ be - cause__ I was loved by you.__

You were__ my

%S Chorus:

strength when I__ was weak, you were__ my voice when I could- n't speak. You were__ my

11

CALL THE MAN

Words & Music by Andy Hill & Peter Sinfield.

1. Close the door,_____ shut the world a-way, all the fight's gone_ from this
2. I close my eyes,_____ I re-mem-ber when your sweet love_ filled this

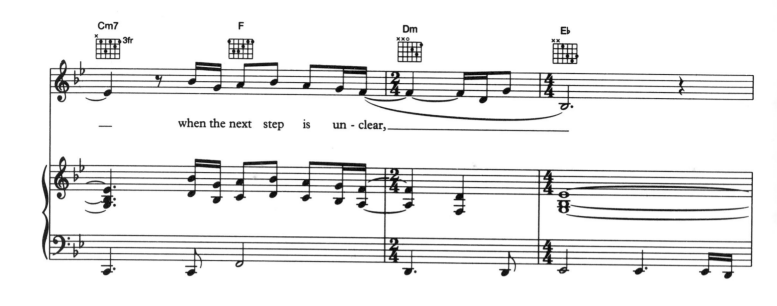

when the next step is un-clear,_____

call the man, he's____ need-ed here, mm._____

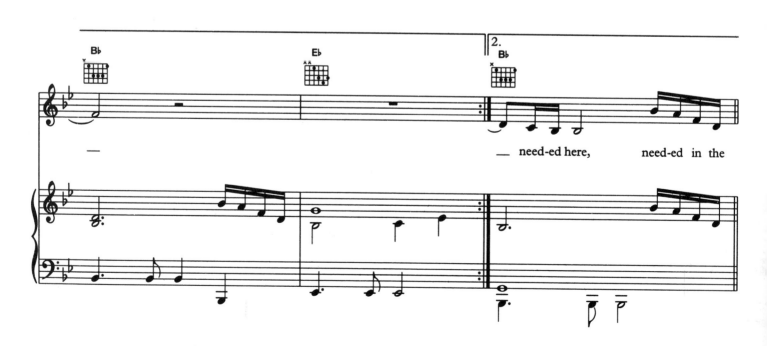

— need-ed here, need-ed in the

....end solo)

Chorus:

Oh_____ call the man who deals_____ in once up-on___ a time,___ may-be he___ can mend___ this bro-ken heart___ of mine,___ shine a light___ up a-head___

18

now the fu - ture is - n't clear, call the man,

call the man, he's need-ed here.

Call the man, he's need-ed here.

Vocal ad lib.

19

He's need-ed here, _____ yeah, yeah. _____

Vocal ad lib.

He's need-ed here,

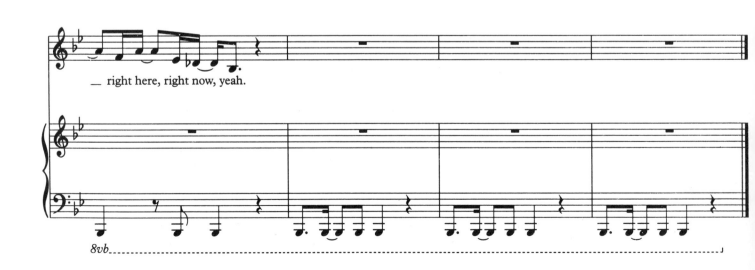

_ right here, right now, yeah.

FALLING INTO YOU

Words & Music by Rick Nowles, Marie-Claire D'Ubalio & Billy Steinberg.

2.3.

Dm   C B♭maj7

___ to___ you. Fall - ing like___ a leaf,_____ fall -

C   Am   B♭   Gm9

- ing like___ a star,_____ find- ing a_____ be - lief_____

C   *To Coda* ⊕ Dm

fall - ing where___ you are._____

C   B♭   C   Dm

Catch___ me, don't let me drop! Love___ me, don't ev- er stop!___

I DON'T KNOW

Music by J. Kapler. Words by Jean Goldman & Philip Galdston.

there _____ when I call your name. ___ I'm sure I

could face _____ the bit - ter cold, _____ but life with - out _

— you, I don't know, I don't know,

repeat ad lib. and fade

— I don't know, ___ I don't know.

30

I REMEMBER L.A.

Words & Music by Tony Colton & Richard Wold.

seems a life - time a - go.___

We were stars___ on___ Sun - set Bou - le - vard.___ What a mo - vie___ we made.___

There were days in the sun
(Verse 2 see block lyric)

that have stayed for - ev - er

young.

Nights when pas - sion was in -

vin - ci - ble. We thought love would nev - er

die._____ There were mo - ments in that life - time that my heart__

still re - plays._____ There were mi - nutes, there were ho -

- urs, there were days._____ There are__

mo - ments I still love__ you that same__ way.__

Verse 2:
I remember goodbye,
I watched your plane out of sight.
Love was over, time to close the book,
Still I go back for one last look.

IT'S ALL COMING BACK TO ME NOW

Words & Music by Jim Steinman.

39

JUST WALK AWAY

Words & Music by Albert Hammond & Marti Sharron.

1. I know I ne-ver loved this way be-fore and no one else has loved me more, with you I've laughed and cried,

I have lived and died, what I would-n't do just to be with you. I

know I must for-get you to go on, I can't hold back my tears too
(Verse 2 see block lyric)

long though life won't be the same, I've got to take the blame and

find the strength I need to let you go. Just walk a-

Just walk a -

way,_____ just say good - bye, don't turn a - round now, you_ may see me

cry,_____ I must-n't fall a - part or show my bro - ken heart,

or the love I feel for you. So walk a - way_____ and close the

48

Verse 2:
There'll never be a moment I'll regret,
I've loved you since the day we met.
For all the love you gave and all the love we made
I know I've got to find the strength to say

LOVE DOESN'T ASK WHY

Words & Music by Philip Galdston, Barry Mann & Cynthia Weil.

when you're in — my arms — I un - der - stand —   we

don't have a voice —   when our hearts make the choi - ces, there's no

1.
plan, it...   it's not in our hands.

2.
we can try.

Love does - n't ask why, _____   it speaks from the heart —

and nev - er ex - plains.— Don't you know— that love does - n't think twice,—

it can come all at once— or whis - per from a dis - tance. So let's

take what we found— and wrap it a - round— us.—

Love does - n't ask why— it speaks from the heart— and nev - er ex - plains_

Verse 2:
Now I can feel what you're afraid to say,
If you give your soul to me.
Will you give too much away,
But we can't let this moment pass us by.
Can't question this chance
Or expect any answers.
We can try,
Maybe we can try.

SEDUCES ME

Music by Dan Hill & John Shead. Words by Dan Hill.

57

night,_____ ev-ery tear that you cry, se - duc - es

me,_____ oh, oh,_____ se - duc - es me, and all that you

do_____ se - duc - es me._____

59

THE LAST TO KNOW

Words & Music by Philip Galdston & Brock Walsh.

Verse 2:
You know how old friends will talk
A secret's hard to keep.
But this girl she says you're seeing
Sure sounds a lot like me.
Still it's not for me to say
If what I heard was true.
And I won't let myself believe a word
Till I hear it from you.

THE POWER OF LOVE

Words & Music by C. deRouge, G. Mende, J. Rush & S. Applegate.

1. The whis-pers in the morn-ing
(Verse 2 see block lyric)

of lov-ers sleep-ing tight,

are roll-ing by like thun-der now

as I look in your eyes.

I hold on to your bo-dy,

and feel each move you make,

your voice is warm and ten-der, a love that

I could_____ not for - sake.

'Cause I'm your la - - dy,_____

and you are my man,_____ when - ev - er you reach_____

___for me, I'll do all that I can.____

The sound of your heart beat - - ing___ made it clear___ sud-den-

ly, the feel-ing that I can't go on___

D.%. al Coda

is light years a - way.___ 'Cause I'm your la-

Coda

The pow - er of love,___

68

Repeat to fade

Verse 2:
Lost is how I'm feeling
Lying in your arms,
When the world outside's too much to take,
That all ends when I'm with you.
Even though there may be times
It seems I'm far away,
Never wonder where I am
'Cause I am always by your side.

THE COLOUR OF MY LOVE

Words & Music by David Foster & Arthur Janov.

own.

I'll draw your arms a-round my waist, then all doubt I shall e-rase,

I'll paint the rain that soft-ly lands on your wind blown hair,

rall.   *a tempo*

I'll trace a hand to wipe your tears,

a look to calm your fears, a sil-hou-ette of dark and light, while we

hold each oth-er___ oh so___ tight. I'll paint a

sun to warm your heart, swear-ing that we'll nev - er part,___

that's the co-lour of___ my love. I'll paint the

truth, show how I feel, try to make you com-plete-ly real,___ I'll use a

learn, _____ so much to try, _____ and with this ring our lies will start,

swear-ing that we'll nev - er part.   I of - fer what you can - not buy____ de -

vot - ed love____ un - til we die,_____

ooh,_____   ooh._____

THINK TWICE

Words & Music by Andy Hill & Pete Sinfield.

1. Don't think I can't feel that there's some - thing wrong,—
(Verse 2 see block lyric)

you've been the sweet - est part— of my life for so long.

I look in your eyes, there's a dis - tant light

and you and I know there'll be a storm to - night.

This is get - ting ser - i - ous,

are you think - in' 'bout you or us. Don't say

Verse 2:
Baby think twice, for the sake of our love
For the memory,
For the fire and the faith
That was you and me.
Babe I know it ain't easy
When your soul cries out for higher ground,
'Cause when you're halfway up
You're always halfway down.

But baby this is serious
Are you thinking 'bout you or us?

1/98 (29706)